How to Use this Book

Firstly, check the learning objectives for this tex

Guided Reading has three stages:

Before **Guided Reading**

Walkthrough

Take the children through the book, encouraging them to talk about the pictures and follow the events of the story. Engage them in the story by asking the questions in the band across the top of each page.

During **Guided Reading**

Observe and Prompt

As the children read the story independently, observe their reading behaviour and encourage them to use their phonic skills and knowledge as they tackle challenges in the text. Check that they are following and understanding the story by asking questions and inviting comments.

Phonic Opportunities

There are specific suggestions for embedding and checking phonic skills and knowledge. This book provides opportunities to focus on initial letters and phonemes, and to sound out and blend phonemes to read CVC words.

After **Guided Reading**

Revisit and Respond

At the back of this book is a list of activities designed to develop the children's response to the story and to reinforce the teaching focus of this book.

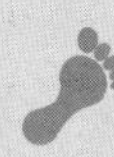

Walkthrough

Let's look at the front cover.
This is a story about Curly.
What kind of creature is Curly?
Curly is playing a game. Can you guess what game he is playing?

Phonic Opportunity

Point to the title.
Point to the initial letters 'H' and 'S' and ask the children what sound they make.

Walkthrough

Let's look at the back cover.
This has the blurb that tells us about the story.

Read the blurb.

What is Curly doing with his fingers?

Phonic Opportunity

Can you see some words in the blurb that start with a 'c'? Point to them.

Hide and Seek

Tony Mitton
Illustrated by Andy Parker

Walkthrough

Let's look at the title page. Everyone read the title with me this time.

Point to the words as you read.

What do you think Curly is doing in this picture?

Phonic Opportunity

Reinforce the initial sounds of the letters 'H' and 'S'.

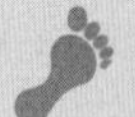

Walkthrough

(Page 2): How many caterpillars can we see?

(Page 3): How many beetles can we see?

This is a counting story. How many creatures do you think we'll find on the next page?

Observe and Prompt

Word Recognition

- (P) Ask children to find the initial 'c' in 'curly' and 'caterpillar' on page 2, and the initial 'b' in 'big' and 'beetle' on page 3.
- (P) Check children are reading 'big' on page 3 using their decoding skills. Can they sound out and blend b-i-g all through the word?
- If the children have difficulty with the other words on these pages, tell them the words and then model how to blend them (but check that children can identify the initial letters and phonemes).

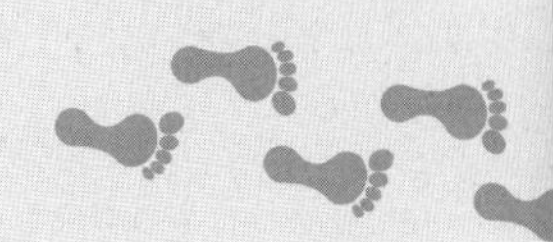

two big beetles

3

Observe and Prompt

Language Comprehension

- Ask the children what Curly has to do to find the beetles.
- Check that the children understand the number of each group of Curly's friends is getting higher as the story goes on.

Walkthrough

You were right! There are three green grasshoppers … and how many slippery snails?

three green grasshoppers

4

Observe and Prompt

Word Recognition

- (P) Check the children can sound out and identify the initial 'g's on page 4 and the initial 's's on page 5.
- (P) Some children may be able to use their decoding skills to read 'three' and 'green'. Can they sound out and blend the phonemes all through these words?
- If the children find it difficult to read the other words on these pages, first check that they can identify and sound out the initial phonemes and then tell them the words, modelling how to blend them.

four slippery snails

5

Observe and Prompt

Language Comprehension

- Check that the children are able to comment on what is happening in the story by asking where Curly finds each group of friends.

Walkthrough

How many ladybirds do you think there are? Count and see if you are right.
How many worms are there?

five little ladybirds

6

Observe and Prompt

Word Recognition

- **P** Check the children can identify and sound out the initial 'l's on page 6 and the initial 'w's on page 7.
- **P** Check that children use their decoding skills to read 'six', sounding out and blending all through the word.
- If the children find it difficult to read any of the other words on these pages, first check they can identify the initial phonemes and then tell them the words, modelling how to blend them.

six wiggly worms

7

 **Observe and Prompt**

Language Comprehension

- How do the children think Curly and his friends are feeling? How do they know?
- Check the children have established the text pattern.

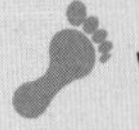

Walkthrough

How are Curly and his friends feeling now? How many friends has Curly got?

Observe and Prompt

Word Recognition

- (P) Ask the children to find all the initial 'l's.
- (P) Check the children can use their decoding skills to read 'lots', sounding out and blending the phonemes all through the word.
- If the children find it difficult to read 'laughing', 'little' and 'friends', tell them these words, but ask them to identify the initial phonemes first.

Revisit and Respond

- Say some number rhymes together (e.g. 1, 2, 3, 4, 5, Once I Caught a Fish Alive).
- Think of some other alliterative animals (e.g. dirty dog).
- Ask the children to tell you what happened in the story in their own words. Compare the retelling with the original text of the story.

Independent Group Activity Work

This book is accompanied by two photocopy masters, one with a reading focus, and one with a writing focus, which support the teaching objectives for this book. The photocopy masters can be found in the *Planning and Assessment Guide.*

PCM Ph2.1 (reading)

PCM Ph2.2 (writing)

You may also like to invite the children to read the story again, during their independent reading (either at school or at home).

ASSESSMENT POINTS

Assess that the children have learnt the main teaching focus of this book by checking that they can:

Word Recognition	Language Comprehension
• identify, sound out and read the initial phonemes in words; • use decoding skills to read the CVC words 'big' and 'six'.	• explain what happened in the story • retell the story in correct sequence.